4/16/94

Dear Saya,
    This story was read to your Daddy and to your Aunt Ann when they were your age -

        Love,
             Grandma xxxx
                      oooo

Bernice Hogan

Now
I lay me down
to wonder . . .

pictures by

Susan Perl

New York   ABINGDON PRESS   Nashville

To My Children,

Carol, Bob, and Susan,

before whose love and imagination,
I bow my own heart in wonder and prayer

What *is* prayer?

Is it always asking for a favor, or always saying "thank you"?

For grownups, perhaps; but those who are not so old can smile at God, and chat, and never even know that some would say they ought to bow their heads, and close their eyes, and say "Amen."

Heavenly Father, now I pray
As I kneel at close of day.

Let me through my window peer
At the stars that burn so clear.

I touch the night so soft and good
Like the velvet of my hood.

Father, God, my thanks I say,
To you, who made the night and day.

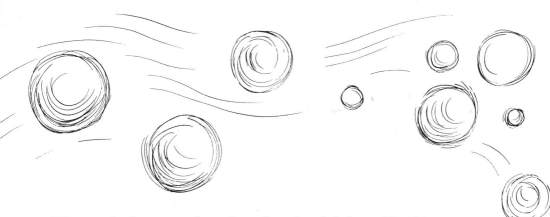

How did you think of a bubble, God?
How did you dream it so?
With colors so white that sparkle so pink,
How did you make it grow?

Did you ever carry a bubble, God?
Then, tell me, how did you know
That children could lift such fairy balls
And that children would love them so?

Blue as the sky on an August day,
White as a snowflake star,
Green as the grass where my bare feet walk,
This is the world God made.

Red as a cardinal spreading his wings,
Gray as a stone I found,
Yellow as pansies nodding their heads,
This is the world God loves.

Please, God,
Please make it sunny.
There's a sparrow to feed,
And a forest to walk,
Daisies to pick,
And a wonderful world to explore.
Please, God,
Please make it sunny.

Showers are delightful chats,
Talks with small raindrops,
Thank you, God, for drops of rain,
And all they whisper about.

I thank you, God,
For wind
  That blows my short red hair
  And makes the long, white hair
    of dandelions to dance away.
I thank you, God,
For wind.

Once God thought of a mother, you,
And then he thought of a father, too;
He sent them scampering children, three,
And now we are a family.

God, who made a snowflake white,
God, who made a star so bright,
May I know you when I pray?
Will you be my friend each day?

Father of a pansy gay,
Father of a sparrow gray,
May I call you "Father," too?
Will you show me what to do?

Lightning's like a candle
swiftly flying by;

Thunder is a lion
roaring in the sky;

Rain is like the stepping
of kindergarten feet;

Sun is gay and laughing
    as I run down the street;

But the best of weather
    is, at least to me,
Rainbow in the heaven,
    promise sent from thee.

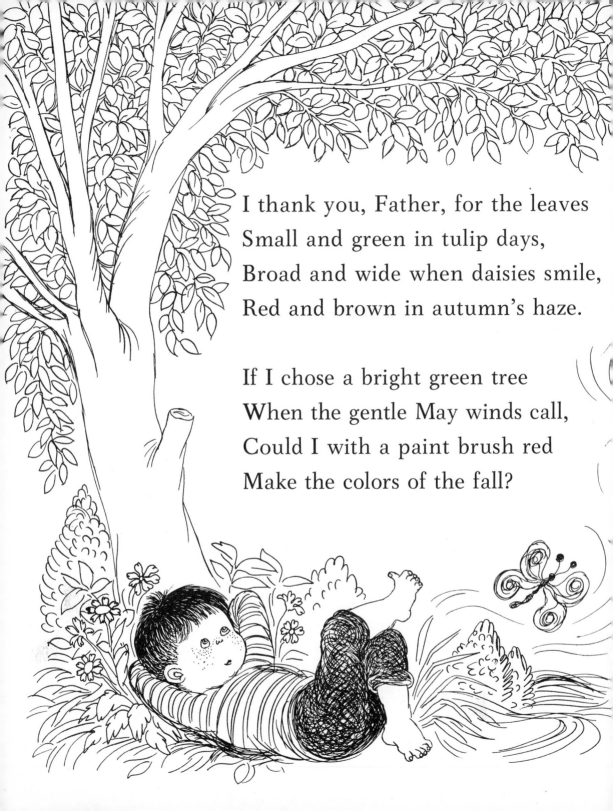

I thank you, Father, for the leaves
Small and green in tulip days,
Broad and wide when daisies smile,
Red and brown in autumn's haze.

If I chose a bright green tree
When the gentle May winds call,
Could I with a paint brush red
Make the colors of the fall?

If when sweaters, mittens come,
When the days of school begin,
Could I pick a crisp brown leaf,
Make it live and green again?

I thank you, Father, for your leaves,
Small and green in tulip days,
I'm glad that only you can make
Trees and leaves and autumn haze.

Now I lay me down to wonder
Why God made the sand and sea,
Why He made the clouds and thunder,
Why He made a child like me.

"Because He loves you, dear," my mother says.
"Now go to sleep."